NO REGARD BEAUREGARD
and the GOLDEN RULE

NO REGARD BEAUREGARD
and the GOLDEN RULE

Written by MELISSA W. ODOM

Illustrated by JAMES RICE

PELICAN PUBLISHING COMPANY
Gretna 1988

Library of Congress Cataloging-in-Publication Data

Odom, Melissa W.
    No Regard Beauregard and the Golden Rule.

    Summary: Beauregard Glover changes his thoughtless
ways after learning about the Golden Rule in Sunday
School.
    [1. Conduct of life—Fiction. 2. Christian life—
Fiction. 3. Stories in rhyme] I. Rice, James,
1934-   ill. II. Title.
    PZ8.3.0287No   1988   [E]   87-36118
    ISBN 0-88289-686-5

Manufactured in the United States of America

Published by Pelican Publishing Company, Inc.
1101 Monroe Street, Gretna, Louisiana 70053

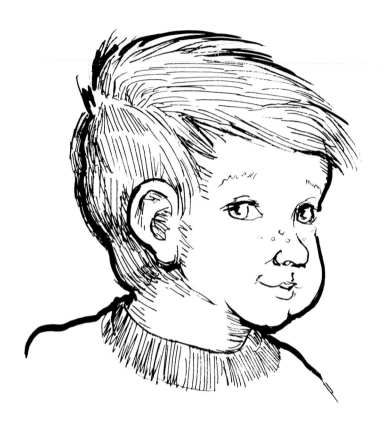

In a tassle-haired top and a freckle-faced cover
Lived a rugged young fellow named Beauregard Glover.
His face was the picture of innocent charm.
Who'd think, underneath, there was mischief or harm?
Now Beau was a youngster of poor reputation
For not thinking of others, and just plain aggravation.

When the cheese was found dried out, unwrapped, and hard
The next sandwich-maker cried, "Ugh! Beauregard!"

When Beau finished bathing, though such times were rare,
The tub was a mudhole with soapsuds and hair.
His towel, wet and wadded, was thrown on the floor.
His jeans, in a heap, were flung over the door.

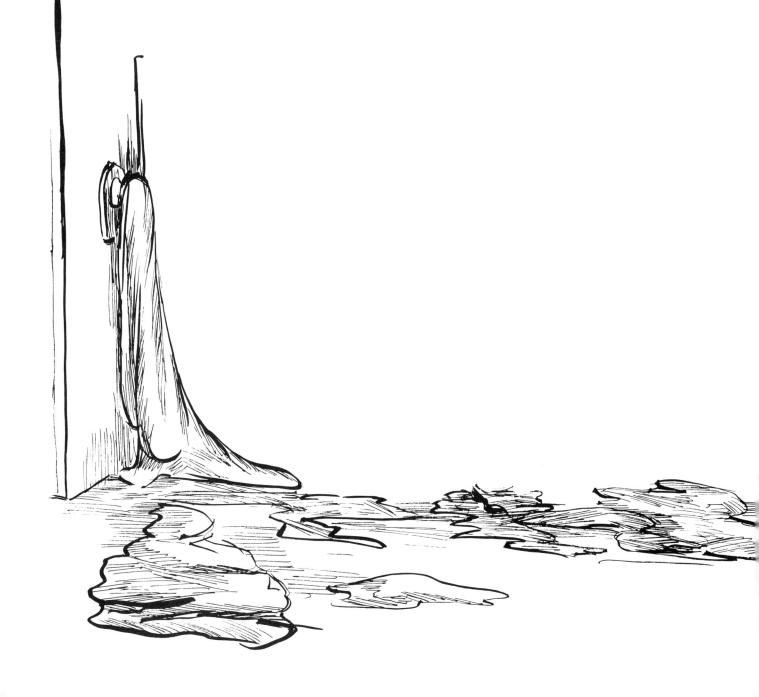

To pick up one thing he gave never a notion,
And when Beauregard left there was chaos, commotion.
On Saturday, early, while his mom slept
Beau snuck out of bed and downstairs he crept.

He knew it was Mom's day to catch up on rest
But his mind was deciding, "Which cartoon is best?"
He turned on the TV quite loud for his hearing
And soon he was watching and laughing and cheering.
In just a short time Dad appeared in the room
With a bleary-eyed glare and a voice full of doom.

"You have no regard, Beauregard, for any other.
This time is for sleeping and rest for your mother.
Have you looked at the clock? See how early it is?"
But Beau shrugged his shoulders and mumbled, "Gee whiz . . ."

When Beauregard finished with things he would borrow
He put off returning them, saying, "Tomorrow . . ."
He left tools in his clubhouse and toys in the garden,
Brushes with paint that would dry out and harden.

While Dad raked leaves in the heat of the day
He ran off with Sparky to frolic and play.

When Grandmother's glasses were not to be found
Beau couldn't be bothered to help look around.
Yes, he'd earned his nickname without trying too hard.
He was called, by his victims, "*No Regard* Beauregard."
Beau tried to make friends, but they didn't last long.
They tired of his rudeness and things he did wrong.

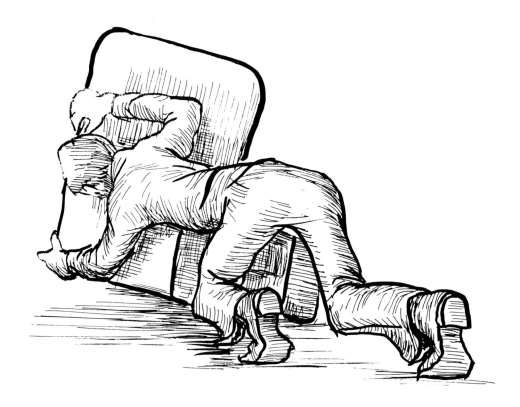

Then, one Sunday morning at Beau's Sunday School,
The teacher was teaching on God's Golden Rule.
"Do unto others," Miss Benton had read,
And for once Beau listened to what the Word said.

The verse taught a lesson he needed to learn —
The way we treat others to us will return.
"I really *don't* think of my family or friends,
Only what's good for *me* — and that's where it ends.

No wonder my friends don't last more than a day.
I demand to be first and to have my own way."

That day when he prayed Beau said, "Help me, Dear Father,
Please show me the way that You'd have me treat others.
I want to do better at home and at school.
Please help me to live by Your Golden Rule."

That week he was different — a pleasant surprise.
His mother and dad could not believe their eyes.
His manners were better, his voice was polite,
And, MOST of the time he was just a delight.
Beau tried to live by the rule that was Gold,
And do all his chores without being told.

His friends were amazed that he offered and shared.
They soon came to realize that Beau really *cared*.
He found out that treating his family and friends
With kindness and love was where friendship begins.

He tries to treat those he meets with regard,
And now he is known as just plain "Beauregard."